This igloo book belongs to:

....

igloobooks

Published in 2019
by Igloo Books Ltd, Cottage Farm, Sywell, NN6 0BJ
www.igloobooks.com

Illustrated by Belinda Strong

Designed by Chris Stanley
Edited by Kathryn Beer

GOL002 0519
4 6 8 10 9 7 5 3
ISBN 978-1-78670-294-4

Printed and manufactured in China

My First
Action
Rhymes

igloobooks

The Wheels on the Bus

The wheels on the bus go round and round,
Round and round, round and round.
The wheels on the bus go round and round,
All day long.

The horn on the bus goes toot, toot, toot,
Toot, toot, toot, toot, toot, toot.
The horn on the bus goes toot, toot, toot,
All day long.

The wipers on the bus go swish, swish, swish,
Swish, swish, swish, swish, swish, swish.
The wipers on the bus go swish, swish, swish,
All day long.
The people on the bus go up and down,
Up and down, up and down.
The people on the bus go up and down,
All day long.

Incy Wincy Spider

Incy Wincy Spider,
Climbed up the waterspout.

Down came the rain,
And washed the spider out.

Out came the sunshine,
And dried up all the rain.

And Incy Wincy Spider,
Climbed up the spout again.

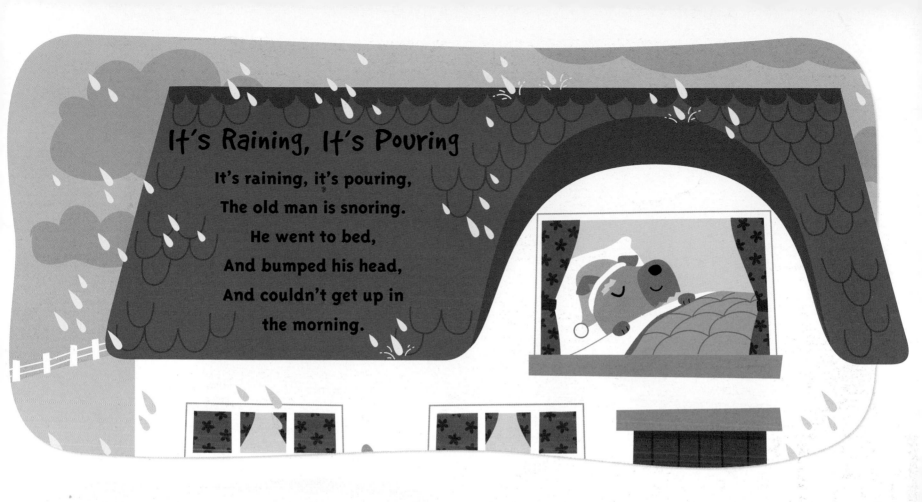

It's Raining, It's Pouring

It's raining, it's pouring,

The old man is snoring.

He went to bed,

And bumped his head,

And couldn't get up in

the morning.

I'm a Little Teapot

I'm a little teapot, short and stout.

Here is my handle, here is my spout.

When I get all steamed up, hear me shout,

"Tip me up and pour me out."

Oranges and Lemons

"Oranges and lemons," say the bells of St. Clement's.

"You owe me five farthings," say the bells of St. Martin's.

"When will you pay me?" say the bells of Old Bailey.

"When I grow rich," say the bells of Shoreditch.

"When will that be?" say the bells of Stepney.

"I do not know," says the great bell at Bow.

"Here comes a candle to light you to bed.

Here comes a chopper to chop off his head."

See-saw, Margery Daw

See-saw, Margery Daw,
Jacky shall have a new master.
He shall have but a penny a day,
Because he can't work any faster.

Ring a Ring o'Roses

Ring a ring o'roses,
A pocket full of posies.
Atishoo, atishoo,
We all fall down.

Pease Porridge Hot

Pease porridge hot, pease porridge cold.

Pease porridge in the pot, nine days old.

Some like it hot, some like it cold.

Some like it in the pot, nine days old.

Pat-a-cake

Pat-a-cake, pat-a-cake, baker's man.

Bake me a cake as fast as you can.

Roll it, pat it and mark it with a 'b',

Put it in the oven for baby and me.

The Grand Old Duke of York

Oh, the grand old Duke of York,

He had ten thousand men.

He marched them up to the top of the hill,

And he marched them down again.

And when they were up, they were up.

And when they were down, they were down.

And when they were only halfway up,

They were neither up nor down.

London Bridge

London Bridge is falling down,

Falling down, falling down.

London Bridge is falling down,

My fair lady.

Two Little Dicky Birds

Two little dicky birds,
Sitting on a wall.
One named Peter,
One named Paul.
Fly away, Peter,
Fly away, Paul.
Come back, Peter,
Come back, Paul.

This Little Piggy

This little piggy went to market,
This little piggy stayed at home.
This little piggy had roast beef,
This little piggy had none.
And this little piggy went,
"Wee, wee, wee," all the way home.

Here We Go Gathering

Here we go gathering nuts in May,
Nuts in May, nuts in May.
Here we go gathering nuts in May,
On a cold and frosty morning.

Who will you have for nuts in May,
Nuts in May, nuts in May?
Who will you have for nuts in May,
On a cold and frosty morning?

Who will you send to fetch her away,
Fetch her away, fetch her away?
Who will you send to fetch her away,
On a cold and frosty morning?

Tom and Jack will fetch her away,
Fetch her away, fetch her away.
Tom and Jack will fetch her away,
On a cold and frosty morning.

Grandma's Spectacles

These are Grandma's spectacles,
This is Grandma's hat.
This is the way she folds her hands,
And lays them on her lap.

Eenie, Meenie, Miney, Moe

Eenie, meenie, miney, moe,
Catch a tiger by the toe.
If he hollers, let him go,
Eenie, meenie, miney, moe.

One Potato, Two Potato

One potato, two potato,
Three potato, four.
Five potato, six potato,
Seven potato more.

Horsey, Horsey

Horsey, horsey, don't you stop.
Just let your feet go clippety-clop.
Your tail goes swish and the wheels go round.
Giddy up, we're homeward bound.

We're not in a hustle, we're not in a bustle.
Don't go tearing up the road.
We're not in a hurry, we're not in a flurry,
And we don't have a very heavy load.

Horsey, horsey, don't you stop.
Just let your feet go clippety-clop.
Your tail goes swish and the wheels go round.
Giddy up, we're homeward bound.

Five Fat Sausages

Five fat sausages sizzling in a pan,
One went pop and the others went bang.

Four fat sausages sizzling in a pan,
One went pop and the others went bang.

Three fat sausages sizzling in a pan,
One went pop and the others went bang.

Two fat sausages sizzling in a pan,
One went pop and the other went bang.

One fat sausage sizzling in a pan,
One went pop and none went bang.

No fat sausages sizzling in a pan.

Dingly, Dangly Scarecrow

I'm a dingly, dangly scarecrow,
With a flippy, floppy hat.
I can shake my hands like this,
I can shake my feet like that.

The Bear Went Over the Mountain

The bear went over the mountain,
The bear went over the mountain,
The bear went over the mountain,
To see what he could see.

And all that he could see,
And all that he could see,
Was the other side of the mountain,
The other side of the mountain,
The other side of the mountain,
Was all that he could see.

A Sailor Went to Sea

A sailor went to sea, sea, sea,

To see what he could see, see, see,

And all that he could see, see, see,

Was the bottom of the deep, blue sea, sea, sea.

A Farmer Went Trotting

A farmer went trotting upon his bay mare,
Bumpety, bumpety, bump.
With his daughter behind, so rosy and fair,
Lumpety, lumpety, lump.
A raven cried, "Croak," and they went tumbling down,
Bumpety, bumpety, bump.
The mare hurt her knees and the farmer his crown,
Lumpety, lumpety, lump.
The mischievous raven flew laughing away,
Bumpety, bumpety, bump.
And vowed he would serve them the same the next day,
Lumpety, lumpety, lump.

Here is the Church

Here is the church,
Here is the steeple.
Open the doors,
And see all the people.

The Ants Go Marching

The ants go marching one by one,

Hurrah, hurrah.

The ants go marching one by one,

Hurrah, hurrah.

The ants go marching one by one,

The little one stops to suck her thumb,

And they all go marching down,

To the ground,

To get out of the rain.

Boom, boom, boom, boom.

The ants go marching two by two,

Hurrah, hurrah.

The ants go marching two by two,

Hurrah, hurrah.

The ants go marching two by two,

The little one stops to tie her shoe,

And they all go marching down,

To the ground,

To get out of the rain.

Boom, boom, boom, boom.